CRAIG-Y-NOS PREPARATORY SCHOOL
Murton Grange, Clyne Common,
Swansea, SA3 3JB.
Telephone: Bishopston (044 128) 4288

THE MAGIC BUS
INSIDE THE HUMAN BODY

By Joanna Cole   Illustrated by Bruce Degen

KINGFISHER BOOKS

The author and illustrator wish to thank Dr Arnold J. Capute,
Associate Professor of Pediatrics, Director, Division of Child Development,
Johns Hopkins University of Medicine, for his help in preparing this book.

Kingfisher Books, Grisewood & Dempsey Ltd,
Elsley House, 24–30 Great Titchfield Street,
London W1P 7AD

First published in this edition in the UK
in 1990 by Kingfisher Books
Published by arrangement with SCHOLASTIC INC.

BRITISH LIBRARY CATALOGUING-IN-PUBLICATION DATA
Cole, Joanna, 1944–
Inside the human body.
1. Man. Body
I. Title   II. Bruce Degen   III. Series
612

ISBN 0 86272 629 8

Printed in Spain

It all began when Ms Frizzle
showed our class a filmstrip
about the human body.
We knew trouble was about to start,
because we knew Ms Frizzle
was the strangest teacher in the school.

YOUR BODY IS MADE OF CELLS
by Rachel

Your body seems to be all one piece, but actually it is made of trillions of tiny pieces, called cells.

MY BODY IS MADE OF TRILLIONS OF CELLS.

So is MINE!

The very next day, The Friz made us do an experiment on our own bodies.

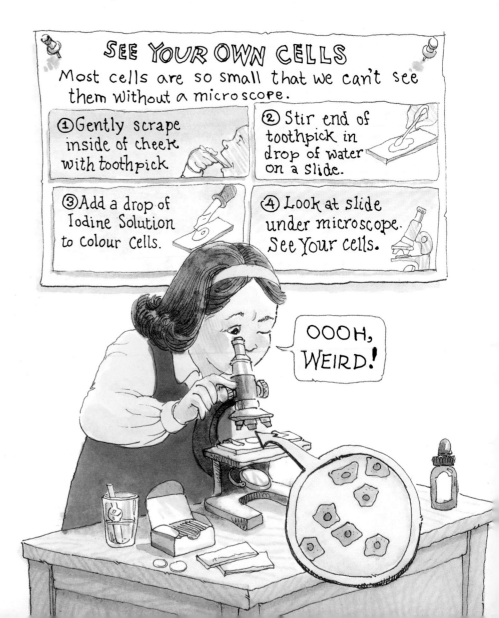

SEE YOUR OWN CELLS

Most cells are so small that we can't see them without a microscope.

① Gently scrape inside of cheek with toothpick

② Stir end of toothpick in drop of water on a slide.

③ Add a drop of Iodine Solution to colour cells.

④ Look at slide under microscope. See your cells.

OOOH, WEIRD!

Then she announced that we were going on a class trip to the science museum. We were going to see an exhibit about how our bodies get energy from the food we eat.

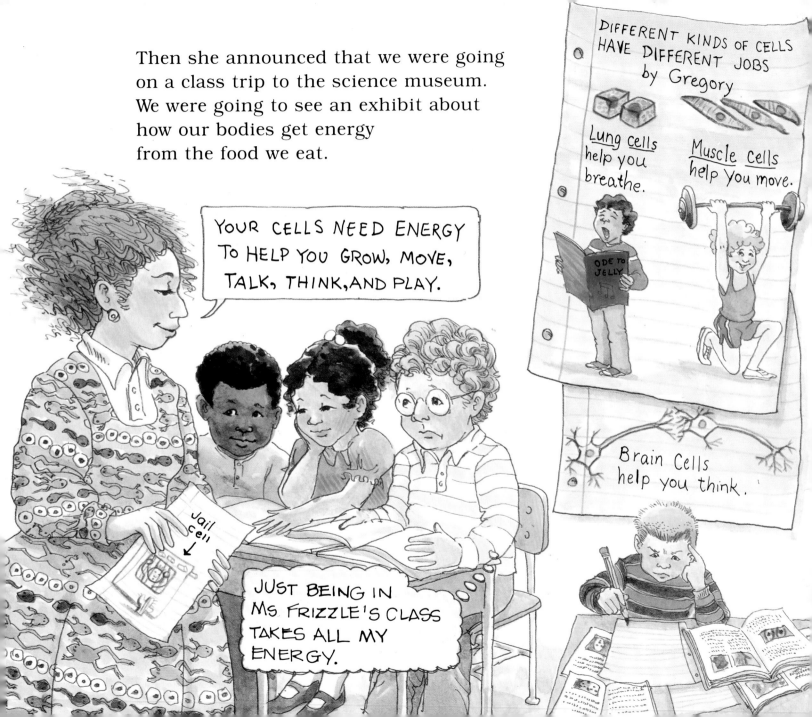

YOUR CELLS NEED ENERGY TO HELP YOU GROW, MOVE, TALK, THINK, AND PLAY.

Jail cell →

JUST BEING IN MS. FRIZZLE'S CLASS TAKES ALL MY ENERGY.

DIFFERENT KINDS OF CELLS HAVE DIFFERENT JOBS
by Gregory

Lung cells help you breathe.

ODE TO JELLY

Muscle cells help you move.

Brain cells help you think.

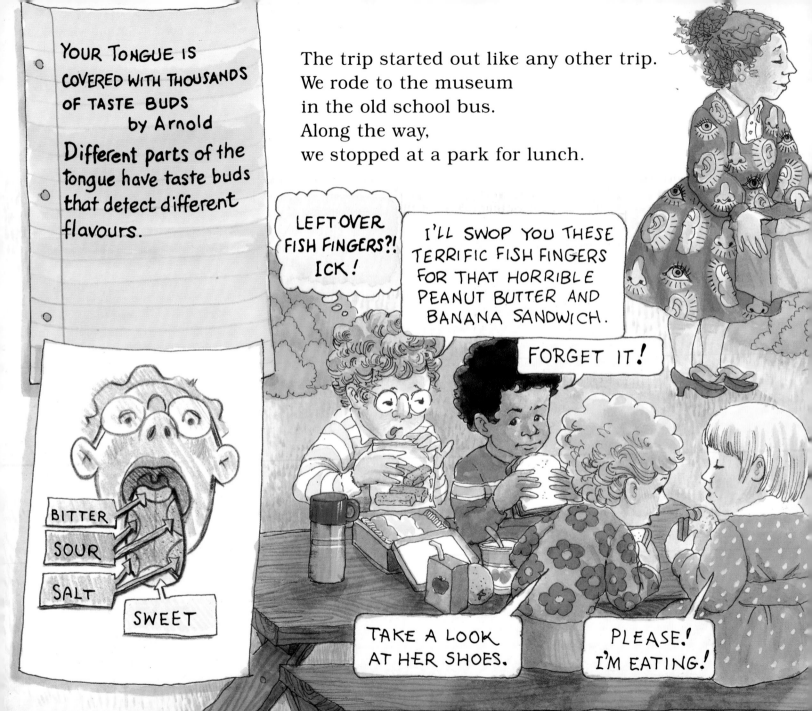

When it was time to go,
everyone got back on the bus—
everyone but Arnold.
He was still at the picnic table,
daydreaming and eating
a bag of Cheesie-Weesies.

WHEN YOU EAT, YOUR BODY <u>DIGESTS</u> THE FOOD SO YOUR CELLS CAN USE IT TO MAKE ENERGY.

YOUR BODY NEEDS GOOD FOOD
by Carmen
For high energy and good growing power eat lots of:

Fresh fruits and Vegetables

Milk and Milk products

Whole grain cereal and Pasta

Lean Meats, Fish, Poultry, AND eggs

AND <u>NOT</u> TOO MUCH JUNK FOOD!

A SCIENCE WORD
by Dorothy Ann

<u>Digestion</u> comes from a word that means to divide. When food is digested it is divided into smaller and smaller parts.

"Hurry up, Arnold!" called Ms Frizzle. She reached for the ignition key, but instead she pushed a strange little button nearby.

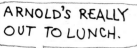
ARNOLD'S REALLY OUT TO LUNCH.

At once, we started shrinking and spinning through the air.

From inside, we couldn't see what was happening. All we knew was that we landed suddenly...

GULP! HEY, WHERE'S THE BUS?

and then we were going down a dark tunnel.
We had no idea where we were.
But, as usual, Ms Frizzle knew.
She said we were inside a human body,
going down the oesophagus—
the tube that leads from the throat
to the stomach.
Most of us were too upset
about leaving Arnold behind
to pay much attention.

WHERE'S ARNOLD?

HE GOT LEFT!

THAT'S WHAT HAPPENS WHEN YOU EAT JUNK FOOD!

I THOUGHT WE WERE GOING TO THE MUSEUM.

THERE'S BEEN A SLIGHT CHANGE OF PLANS... WE'RE BEING DIGESTED INSTEAD.

FOOD GOES TO YOUR STOMACH THROUGH THE OESOPHAGUS
by Wanda
The food does not just fall down.
It is pushed along by muscle actions the way toothpaste is squeezed out of a tube. That's why you can swallow even when you are upside down.

MUSCLES SQUEEZE TO PUSH FOOD TO YOUR STOMACH

WHY ARE THE INTESTINES COILED UP?
by John
In an adult the intestines are 7.5 metres (25 feet) long. If they were stretched out straight, a person would have to be as tall as a house.

STOMACH

FOOD GOES FROM THE STOMACH TO THE SMALL INTESTINE

WASTE GOES OUT THROUGH THE LARGE INTESTINE

The small intestine was
a coiled-up hollow tube.
The inner walls of the tube were covered
with tiny "fingers" called *villi.*
"In the *villi* are tiny blood vessels.
Food molecules are taken into
these blood vessels,"
said Ms Frizzle.
"Once the food is in the blood,
it can travel all over the body."

We felt ourselves getting even smaller,
and Ms Frizzle started driving
into one of the *villi.*
She was going straight into a blood vessel!

WHAT IS BLOOD MADE OF?
by Molly

A little more than half the blood is a yellowish fluid called PLASMA.
The rest of the blood is made of floating cells.

PLASMA
BLOOD CELLS

25 0,000,000

WHY IS BLOOD RED?
by Shirley

Without a microscope, blood looks red because there are so many red blood cells in it!
In every drop of blood there are 250 million red blood cells.

Now we were in the blood,
but it did not look red.
"Blood is not just a red liquid,"
explained Ms Frizzle.
"Blood is made of cells,
floating in a clear fluid."
"Those cells look like red rubber saucers!"
someone called out.
"Those are red blood cells," Ms Frizzle said.
"Red blood cells carry oxygen from the lungs
to all the cells of the body."

DID YOU SEE THAT?

RED BLOOD CELLS CARRY OXYGEN

FOOD MOLECULES

1   2

WHITE BLOOD CELLS

In the lungs, the red cells picked up fresh oxygen.

WE GET NEW OXYGEN FROM THE AIR EACH TIME WE BREATHE IN.

WE GET RID OF A WASTE GAS—CARBON DIOXIDE—EACH TIME WE BREATHE OUT.

TO THE LEFT LUNG

AIR SAC

NEW OXYGEN

CARBON DIOXIDE

LEFT LUNG

MY HEART IS POUNDING.

TAKE A DEEP BREATH. YOU'LL BE OK.

BLOOD GOES ROUND
AND ROUND
     by Michael
In less than a minute
your blood makes
a trip all around
your body.
     This is called the
circulation of the
blood.

ONE MORE SCIENCE WORD
     by Dorothy Ann
Circulate comes from
a word that means
"to circle". Blood
circulates – circles –
all around your body.

From the lungs, our red blood cells
carried us back to the heart.
This time we were on the left side
of the heart—the side that pumps
fresh blood back to the body again.
"Kids, it looks as if these red
blood cells are on their way to
the brain," said Ms Frizzle.

LOOK! WHEN THE
RED BLOOD CELLS
PICK UP OXYGEN, THEY
TURN BRIGHT RED.

FROM RIGHT LUNG

AIR SAC

CLASS, THOSE BRAIN CELLS NEED MORE OXYGEN!

WE'LL NEVER GET HOME UNLESS WE FIND THE BUS.

MAYBE WE'LL FIND IT IN THE BRAIN.

FRESH BLOOD TO UPPER BODY

FROM LEFT LUNG

3rd Chamber

4th Chamber

FRESH BLOOD TO LOWER BODY

WHICH WAY BACK TO SCHOOL?

USE YOUR BRAIN.

YOUR BRAIN IS ALWAYS WORKING
by Alex
Even when you're sleeping, your brain controls your heartbeat, breathing, and other body functions.

When we reached the brain,
we let go of our red blood cells
and squeezed out of the blood vessel.
It was hard to believe that
this wrinkled grey blob was
the control centre of the body.

CHILDREN, WE ARE WALKING ON THE CEREBRAL CORTEX, THE PINKISH GREY, OUTER LAYER OF THE BRAIN. WITHOUT IT WE COULDN'T SEE, HEAR, SMELL, TOUCH, TASTE, TALK, MOVE, OR THINK!

MOTOR CENTRE (TELLS MUSCLES TO MOVE)

SPEECH CENTRE

HEARING CENTRE

YOUR BRAIN NEVER LIES DOWN ON THE JOB.

3:00 A.M. and still at it.

CEREBRAL CORTEX
Controls thinking, moving and the five senses.

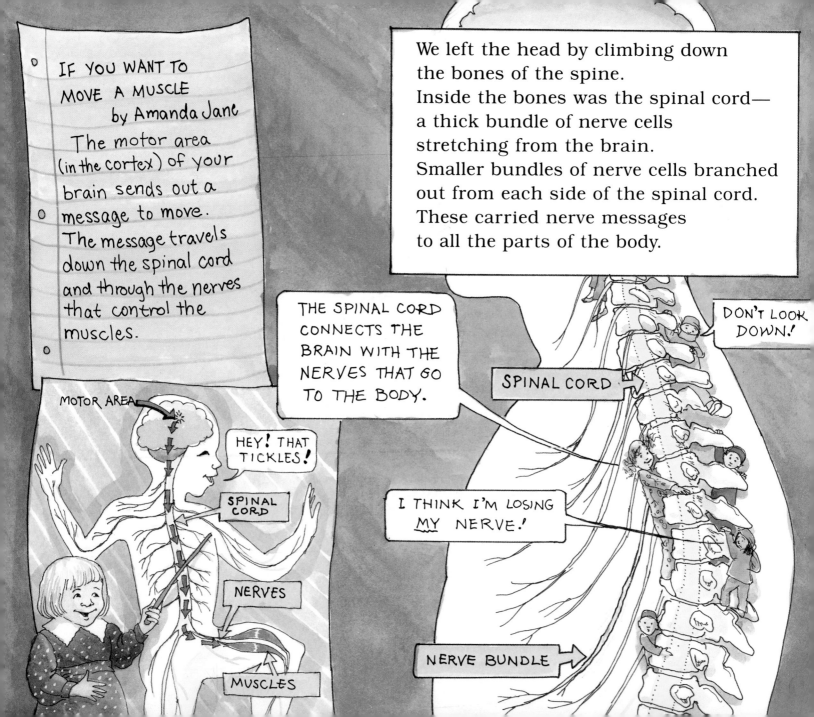

We followed some nerves that went to the leg muscles.
The leg muscles were working hard.
They needed a lot of energy.
They used up a lot of food and oxygen from the blood.
The heart was beating faster to carry fresh blood to the muscle cells.

When we emerged from the bloodsteam,
we were in a huge open space.
"Where are we?" asked a kid.
Ms Frizzle explained,
"Children, this is the nasal cavity."
"The what?" we asked.
"The inside of the nose," said The Friz.
Suddenly, we heard a deafening noise.
It sounded like "Ah-aa-aa-ah!"

A tremendous blast of air
hit the bus full force.
We flew forward,
spinning round and round.

CHILDREN, PREPARE FOR LANDING.
PLEASE REMAIN SEATED UNTIL THE SCHOOL BUS HAS COME TO A COMPLETE STOP.

IS SHE FOR REAL?

A-A-A-AH CHOO!

BLESS YOU!

We were going so fast,
we couldn't see anything,
but we could tell we were getting bigger.
Then—thud!—we landed.
There we were, back at school.
And there was Arnold,
in the school car park,
blowing his nose.

"Arnold!" we said, "the trip was *amazing!*
You should have been there!"

WHERE WERE YOU?

Back in the classroom,
it was business as usual.
Ms Frizzle made us draw
a chart of the human body
for the bulletin board.

THE KIDNEYS
CLEAN YOUR BLOOD
AND MAKE URINE.

THE BLADDER
STORES URINE.

KIDNEYS

BLADDER

LIVER

STOMACH

THE LIVER STORES
VITAMINS AND
DESTROYS POISONS.
IT ALSO MAKES BILE,
A FLUID THAT HELPS
DIGEST FATTY FOODS.

NERVE

BLOOD VESSEL

BONE

MUSCLE

WHAT A TRIP!

I'D LIKE TO GO TO THE LUNGS AGAIN.

I'D RATHER GO TO HAWAII.

BRAIN

NOSE

SPINE

OESOPHAGUS

WINDPIPE

LUNGS

HEART

LIVER

STOMAC

HEY!

THE HEART

TRUE-OR-FALSE TEST

STOP! TAKE THIS TEST!
DO NOT WATCH T.V. ... YET.
DO NOT GET A SNACK ... YET.
DO NOT PLAY A VIDEO
GAME ... YET.

FIRST TAKE THIS TEST.

HOW TO:
Read the sentences below. Decide if each one is true or false. To see if you are correct, check the answers on the opposite page.

QUESTIONS:

1. A school bus can enter someone's body and kids can go on a tour. True or false?

2. Museums are boring. True or false?

3. Arnold should not have tried to get back to school by himself. True or false?

4. Children cannot breathe or talk when they are surrounded by a liquid. True or false?

5. If the children really were as small as cells, we couldn't see them without a microscope. True or false?

6. White blood cells actually chase and destroy disease germs. True or false?

7. Ms Frizzle really knew where Arnold was the whole time. True or false?

ANSWERS:

1. False! That could not happen in real life. (Not even to Arnold.)

   But in this story the author had to make it happen. Otherwise, the book would have been about a trip to a museum, instead of a trip through the body.

2. False! Museums are interesting and fun. But they are not as strange and gross as actually going inside a human body.

3. True! In real life, it would have been safer if Arnold had found a police officer to help.

4. True. If children were *really* inside a blood vessel, they would drown. It must have been magic.

5. True! The pictures in this book show the cells and the children greatly enlarged.

6. True! As unbelievable as it seems, real white blood cells actually behave just like the ones in this book. They even squeeze through the cells of blood vessel walls to capture germs in your organs and tissues.

7. Probably true. No one is absolutely sure, but most people think Ms Frizzle knows *everything*.

PLEASE DO NOT WRITE IN THIS BOOK.

THANK YOU.